MINDFUL MANTRAS

I BELIEVE IN MYSELF!

My name is Poppy and I believe in myself.

By Laurie Wright

Illustrations by Ana Santos

When I have to go out of the room and leave my toy alone, I feel anxious. I'm not sure what to do.

I can warn everyone around to NOT TOUCH IT,

I can hide my toy,

I can just bring it with me.

I can figure out what to do, I believe in myself.

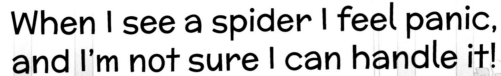

When I see a spider I feel panic,
and I'm not sure I can handle it!

I can leave
the country,

I can try to trap it,

I can walk really far
around it.

I can handle it,
I believe in myself.

When I think there are monsters in my room I feel scared and I'm not sure I can go to sleep.

I can use my stuffies as a monster shield,

I can yell at the monsters that I'm NOT SCARED!!

I can put music on and concentrate on that.

I can go to sleep, I believe in myself.

I can give up
building forever,

I can find a cave to
build in where no one
can find me,

I can forgive my
brother because
he is little.

I can control myself
because I believe in myself.

When I think I might get lost I feel worried and I'm not sure I'll know what to do.

I can click my heels three times and transport myself home,

I can stand still and yell really loudly for help,

I can find an adult I trust and tell them what's wrong.

I'll know what to do if I get lost, I believe in myself.

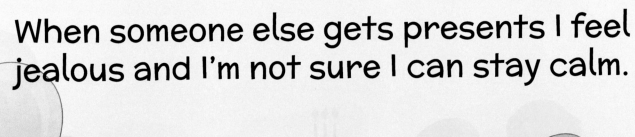

When someone else gets presents I feel jealous and I'm not sure I can stay calm.

I can give myself
a present,

I can wear a hat over
my eyes so I don't
have to see,

I can remember that
everyone gets a turn for
presents and I will too.

I can stay calm,
I believe in myself.

I can sing myself a song about not freaking out,

I can hire a lawyer to make an agreement stating that I get to press all future buttons,

I can take deep belly breaths to calm down.

I won't freak out, I believe in myself!

When we have to cancel plans I feel disappointed and I'm not sure I'll be okay.

I can try
to reschedule,

I can make other
awesome plans,

I can even write down
how I feel or draw
a picture.

I'll be okay,
I believe in myself.

When my cousins go home I feel really sad and I'm not sure I will ever feel happy again.

I can chase
after their car,

I can build cousins
to play with,

I can even call them
on the phone to tell them
I miss them.

I'll be happy again,
I believe in myself!

When I have a new teacher I feel shy
and I'm not sure I'll be able to talk to her.

I can hide
behind bookshelves,

I can zip my head
in my sweatshirt,

I can even be really
brave and look at her.

I'll be able to talk to her
eventually, I believe in myself.

When there are weird sounds in my house I feel nervous and I'm not sure I'll be able to ever leave my room.

I can hide under blankets so I can't hear any noises,

I can sing loudly so I can't hear the noises,

I could even get my detective kit out and figure out what the sounds are.

I'll be able to leave my room, I believe in myself.

Sometimes I feel anxious, panic, scared, frustrated, worried, jealous, angry, disappointed, sad, shy, or nervous.
But it's okay because

... I believe in myself!

My name is

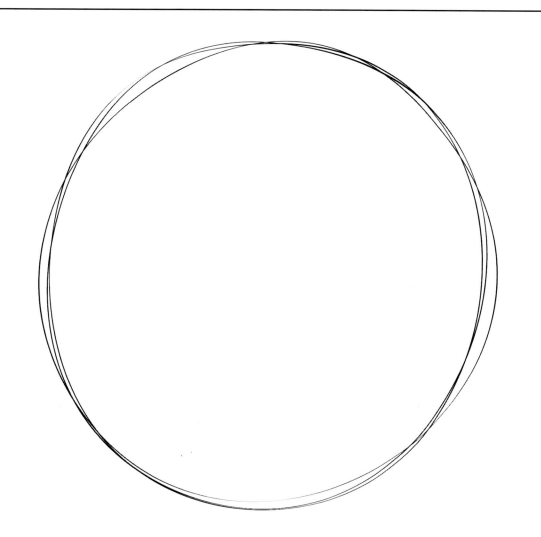

... and I believe in myself!

Dear Readers,

After reading this book you've realized that you believe in yourself too, just like Poppy does, even when you feel unsure. By saying to yourself often "I believe in myself!" it will soon become something you think all the time, and you will feel more confident, knowing how great you are!

Now, I have a question for you. Do you ever want to give up, without even trying? Do you wonder what the point is since things seem SO HARD? If you say YES to those questions, you will enjoy reading the book 'I Will Try' in the Mindful Mantras Series. (here is a little secret: sometimes adults want to give up without even trying too!) In this book you will learn some new words for BIG feelings, that will help you to handle them, if you're up for the challenge!

Get it now, and see if Reeny reminds you of anyone you know!

~Laurie

Laurie Wright

Laurie Wright is a speaker, author, and educator who is passionate about helping children increase their positive self-talk and improve their mental health. Laurie speaks to parents, teachers, has given a TEDx talk, created resources and has written 5 books, all to further the cause of improving the self-esteem of our children. Laurie is a huge advocate for children's mental health and works every day to improve the way we interact with kids, and to help them learn to handle all of their emotions!

Ana Santos

Ana is a creative and innate illustrator and she feels very comfortable and inspired by all the challenges and areas that incorporate illustration and design. Graduated in graphic design, she dicovered her vocation for Arts as a child. Ana has already several years of experience in graphic design and illustration and she has already illustrated several edited children's books for people and publishers around the world! Ana is an artist attentive to new technologies working on many internet platforms as a freelancer.

Made in the USA
Lexington, KY
15 June 2018